Stormy
Waters

Pete Guppy

SURVIVAL

in association with

nasen
Helping Everyone Achieve

NASEN House, 4/5 Amber Business Village, Amber Close, Amington,
Tamworth, Staffordshire B77 4RP

Rising Stars UK Ltd.
22 Grafton Street, London W1S 4EX
www.risingstars-uk.com

Text © Rising Stars UK Ltd.

The right of Pete Guppy to be identified as the author of this work has
been asserted by him in accordance with the Copyright, Design and
Patents Act, 1988.

Published 2009

Cover design: Roger Warham
Cover image: Helene Rogers/Alamy
Text design and typesetting: Roger Warham
Publisher: Gill Budgell
Editorial consultant: Lorraine Petersen

British Library Cataloguing in Publication Data.

A CIP record for this book is available from the British Library.

ISBN: 978-1-84680-599-8

Printed in the UK by CPI Bookmarque, Croydon, CR0 4TD

Mixed Sources
Product group from well-managed
forests and other controlled sources
www.fsc.org Cert no. TT-COC-002227
© 1996 Forest Stewardship Council

Chapter 1

Nick picked up the bottle and drank from it. The whisky hit the back of his throat like fire and burnt its way down.

He sat back and gazed around the big room. He was quickly getting drunk and slowly getting angry.

Suddenly, the door of the room opened.

"What the hell are you doing in here?

You should be in the party," said
Mr Jackson.

Nick took another swig. "What's it got to
do with you?" he said.

"What did you say?" asked Mr Jackson.

"I said what's it got to do with you.
Why don't you get your ears cleaned out?"
said Nick.

Mr Jackson stepped into the room.
"Don't you be so damn cheeky. This is my
house and you're drinking my whisky.
Now put the whisky down and get out!"
he yelled.

Nick got to his feet and threw the bottle
against the wall. Glass and whisky went all
over the room.

"There's your whisky. Lick it up if you
want it," said Nick.

Mr Jackson went red in the face. He
grabbed Nick and dragged him out of
the room.

"Get out of my house!" he yelled.

Nick kicked and punched as he was being dragged along. "Get your hands off me!" he shouted.

"Not until you're out of my house. I don't know why my son asked you to his party. You don't fit in here," said Mr Jackson.

"I'm glad I don't fit in here. I hate rich people like you!" yelled Nick.

"I'm rich because I've worked hard all my life. You've got nothing because you're just like your dad. Too much drink, and too little work," said Mr Jackson.

"You pig. Don't you say that about my dad!" yelled Nick.

Mr Jackson pushed him out of the front door. Nick fell into the garden.

Mr Jackson looked down at him and said, "Now listen to me, you lout. Stay away from my house. Stay away from my whisky. And stay away from my Tim.

"I don't want him ending up like you!"
Then the door was slammed shut.

Nick sat on the ground looking up at the big house. He was angry and upset. Angry about what had been said about his dad. Angry about being kicked out. And upset that no one from the party had come to see if he was all right. He got to his feet.

"I know why none of you came to help me. You've got no guts!" he yelled.

He bent down and picked up a brick. This would make them come outside. But as he stood up, he felt dizzy and a bit sick. He dropped the brick and put his hands to his head.

He knew it was no good. He knew why they hadn't come out to help him.

It was because he wasn't like the rest of them. They all came from rich families with lots of money. They lived in big houses with big gardens. They went to school in big cars.

And he didn't.

But why hadn't Tim come out to help him? It was Tim who had asked him to the party.

Nick put his hands in his pockets and began walking away from the house. Then he stopped and looked back at the house.

"_____ off, Tim. I never wanted to come to your stinking party. You're just the same as the rest of them. You're no friend of mine!" he shouted.

Chapter 2

It had been a crap party, full of posh kids with posh voices. He didn't fit in, and they let him know it. That's why he'd gone looking round the house.

That's when he'd found the whisky. His dad had told him that whisky makes you feel better. But it hadn't.

Nick stood looking at the house.

"I'll get back at you one day, Jackson. Just you wait and see. I'll teach you to kick me out of your house and say things about my dad!" he shouted.

Then a shadow came running across the grass towards him. Was it Mr Jackson coming after him? He picked up a stick. He couldn't see who it was but he felt better with something in his hand.
It wasn't Mr Jackson.

"Are you all right, Nick?" asked Tim.

"_____ off. What do you care?" said Nick. He dropped the stick and walked away.

Tim ran up to him. "Look. I'm sorry you got kicked out. But I couldn't help you," he said.

"You mean you didn't want to help me. Now _____ off and leave me alone," said Nick.

Tim put his hand on Nick's arm. "There was nothing I could do," he said.

Nick pushed Tim's hand away. "Get back to your posh mates at your posh party," he said.

"But you're my mate," said Tim.

"No, I'm not. Mates help each other. You didn't help me when I got kicked out of the house," said Nick.

"But I wasn't in the house. I was next door getting something for the party. When I came back my dad told me all about it. I sneaked out of the house as soon as I could," said Tim.

"Well you can just sneak back in again," said Nick.

Nick walked to the end of the long garden. He stepped onto the path that ran alongside a river.

"Where are you going?" asked Tim.

"For a walk. Leave me alone," said Nick.

Tim ran up and said, "Come on, Nick. Why are you still in such a bad mood?"

Nick turned round and Tim could see the anger in his eyes. "I'll tell you why I'm in a bad mood. I'm in a bad mood because I've just been kicked out of your house. I'm in a bad mood because you've got everything and I've got nothing."

He grabbed Tim and made him look back. "Look. Look at your house. It's so _____ big it looks more like a castle than a house. Look at your garden. You could get two football pitches in it. And you've got a river at the bottom of it. And you've got two big cars. And you've got a rich dad who'll get you everything you want," he ranted.

Nick let go of Tim but he went on talking. "Well you see, Tim. I haven't got any of those things. I live in a little flat that hasn't got a garden at all. My dad is out of work most of the time. We haven't got a car. And we haven't got a bloody river."

Nick pushed his finger at Tim's chest and said, "You've got everything and I've got nothing. That's why I'm in a bad mood. Now have you got any more daft questions you want to ask me?"

Nick turned and began walking along the path. Tim followed him. A full moon came out from behind the clouds. Its silvery light was so clear that Nick could see the ripples on the water. He saw a boat as well. It was tied up to the bank.

"Well, well, well. What have we got here?" asked Nick.

"It's my dad's boat," said Tim.

"So. A big house, a big garden, two big cars, and a boat as well. Where do you keep the helicopter?" said Nick.

"It's only a small boat and it's old. We can only use it on the river. It wouldn't be safe out at sea," said Tim.

"Oh, dear. What a shame," said Nick.

Chapter 3

Nick jumped onto the boat. "Come on. Don't be chicken," he said.

"I'm not chicken," said Tim.

"Yes, you are. Chick, chick, chick, chicken," said Nick.

"Shut up. Someone will hear you," said Tim.

Nick ran round the boat.

"Chick, chick, chick, chicken," he said again. Tim jumped onto the boat.

"That's better. "Now you can show me around," said Nick. He went over to the cabin and put his face against the window. The moon was still out and he could see some boxes inside. "What's inside the boxes?" he asked.

"Food and drink," said Tim. "My dad's going up-river tomorrow. He's taking some friends with him."

Nick looked at the boxes and grinned.

"Come on, then. Tell me some more about the boat," said Nick.

"What do you want to know?" asked Tim.

"How do you get it started?" asked Nick.

"You need a key. You can't start it without one," said Tim.

"Have you got a key?" asked Nick.

Tim didn't like the questions.

He didn't like the smell of whisky on Nick's breath, or the look on his face. "No. I haven't got a key. My dad's got one and there's…" Tim stopped talking. He knew he had just made a big mistake.

Nick came up to him. "Go on. What were you going to say about a key?"

"I wasn't going to say anything," said Tim.

"Yes, you were. You were just going to tell me where there's a key," said Nick.

"No, I wasn't," said Tim.

Nick grabbed him and pushed him against the cabin. "Come on. Where's the other key?" he shouted.

Tim didn't say anything. Nick pushed him to the side of the boat.

"Look. I've been kicked out of your house tonight. If you don't want me to kick you into the river, tell me where the key is," yelled Nick.

Tim cried out, "OK, OK. I'll tell you."

"Go on then. Where is it?" asked Nick.

"It's in the cabin. We keep one in the cabin just in case my dad can't find his," said Tim.

Nick grinned. "That's better," he said.

"But the cabin's locked," said Tim.

"That's OK. We've got some padlocks like that at home. Let's see if one of these will fit," said Nick, taking some keys out of his pocket. Nick tried some of the keys in the padlock but he couldn't get it open.

"Come on. Let's get off the boat," said Tim.

Nick just grinned and said, "I'm not beaten yet. I'll just try these last two." He put the last key in the lock. Click!

"That's better. Now, let's see what we've got in here," he said.

Nick went inside and opened up one of the boxes.

Then he took out one of the bottles. Tim stood in the doorway. "What are you going to do?" he asked.

"I'll tell you what I'm going to do. I'm going to have a party on your dad's boat," said Nick.

Tim didn't look happy.

"Don't look so sad. You asked me to come to your party. Now I'm asking you to come to my party," said Nick.

Tim said, "My dad may be looking for me. He'll go mad if he finds us on his boat."

"Your dad's already mad," said Nick. He took the top off the bottle of whisky and had a drink.

"Come on, Tim. Have a drink of whisky. It's my party," said Nick.

Tim shook his head.

Nick said, "I'm getting _____ off with you. It's my party. So start drinking."

"No," said Tim.

Nick grabbed Tim by the arm and said, "Are you going to drink this whisky or do I have to push the bottle down your throat?"

"Let go of me. I don't want to drink whisky. I just want to get off the boat," said Tim.

He tried to get away but Nick was too strong for him. He grabbed Tim by the hair and pulled him down onto his knees. Then he bent Tim's head back with one hand and tried to push the bottle of whisky into his mouth.

"Come on, Tim. You can do it," he said. Tim kept his mouth shut for as long as he could but he couldn't breathe.

Nick had one arm round his neck and was still pushing the bottle at him.

At last, Tim opened his mouth to get some air. But all he got was whisky. Some went down his throat and some went up his nose. He still couldn't breathe.

Nick thought it was funny.

"There you are. I knew you'd have a drink with me," he said.

He took his arm away from Tim's neck. Tim lay there gasping for air and feeling sick. Then he got up onto his hands and knees and stayed there panting like a dog.

Nick said, "Very good. First of all you were a chicken and now you're a dog. You should be on TV with an act like that."

Chapter 4

Tim was still on his hands and knees. He felt like kicking Nick over the side of the boat. But Nick was two years older, and stronger than he was.

He looked up at Nick. "My dad's right. You are a yob. Just a yob and a bully," he said.

"Shut up," said Nick.

Tim couldn't stop himself. "Yob!" he yelled at Nick.

Nick kicked Tim's arm. "Just shut up or I'll kick you again," he said.

Tim fell onto the deck and didn't say a word.

"Well, now. Seeing as we've got the party started. Let's see if we can get the boat started as well," said Nick. He put his foot on Tim's chest.

"Now be a good boy and tell me where the key is," he said.

Tim tried to get free but Nick pushed harder with his foot.

"It's on the shelf," gasped Tim.

Nick took his foot away and went into the cabin. He got the key from the shelf and went to start the boat. He turned the key but nothing happened. He tried again but still the engine wouldn't start. Nick looked across at Tim.

"What's the matter with it? Why won't it start?" he asked.

"I don't know," said Tim.

"Yes, you do. It's your dad's boat. You know how it works," said Nick.

Tim sat still and said nothing. Nick went over to him.

"Come on, rich boy. How do I get this boat started?" he asked. Tim still sat there and said nothing.

"OK then. I'll *make* you tell me," said Nick.

Tim put up his hands but Nick didn't try to hit him. He just ran over to the side of the boat and untied the ropes. The boat began drifting into the middle of the river.

"You prat! Now we'll be swept down-river. It's only three miles to the sea," said Tim

Nick just stood there with a big smile on his face.

"Well then. You'd better help me start the boat, rich boy," he said.

Tim knew that if they didn't get the engine started they couldn't steer the boat. They would just drift along until they crashed into something. Or be swept out to sea.

But could he trust Nick to turn the boat round?

Tim got to his feet and went over to the cabin.

"You have to put this switch down to let the petrol out of the tank. Then you turn the key to start the engine," he said.

"Well let's do it, Timmy boy," said Nick.

After three turns of the key the engine burst into life. Nick cheered and held onto the wheel.

"Let's go and see what the sea looks like, rich boy," he said.

"Don't be stupid," said Tim.

"Turn the boat round and tie it up."

"No way. I'm off to the seaside for an ice-cream," said Nick as he took another swig from the bottle.

Tim tried to get him away from the wheel, but Nick punched him on the arm.

"You try that again and I'll hit you again," said Nick.

Tim tried again and Nick hit him. There was a cracking sound as Tim fell backwards onto the deck. As he lay there groaning with pain, he knew his left arm was broken.

"Come on. Get up. I need you to help me make this boat go faster," said Nick.

"My arm's broken. You've broken my arm!" cried Tim. Nick just turned the wheel of the boat and went across the river. Then he turned it back again.

"This is great fun, Timmy boy. Now, how do you make it go faster?" he asked.

Tim said nothing. He just lay on the deck.

Nick was just about to shout again when the engine stopped. He looked at Tim and said, "Come on, get this thing started again. I'm having a great time."
Tim stayed on the deck, curled up in pain.

"Come on, Tim. Get up here and give me a hand," said Nick.

"How can I give you a hand when you've broken my bloody arm?" yelled Tim.

The boat was now drifting quickly down the river.

"Come on, Tim. Stop messing about. We need to get the engine started," said Nick.

"I'm not messing about. Look at my arm. It's broken. Look at the shape of it!" shouted Tim. Nick looked at the broken arm. And for the first time he saw just how much pain Tim was in.

Then he looked around as the boat drifted down-river, getting closer to the sea.

He turned the key again and again, but the engine wouldn't start. Nick banged his fist into the door of the cabin.

"What's the matter with it?" he yelled.

"I think we've run out of petrol. My dad only keeps a drop in the tank when the boat is tied up," said Tim.

"Well, that's a stupid thing to do," said Nick.

"No, it isn't. If the boat gets stolen, it means it can't be taken very far before it runs out of petrol," said Tim.

"So why didn't you tell me this when we set off?" asked Nick.

"You wouldn't have listened to me if I had told you," said Tim.

Nick looked around as they drifted down the river. He was still drunk, and each time he turned his head he swayed about on his feet. But even through his whisky haze he could see they had a problem.

"Have you got your mobile with you?" he asked Tim.

"It's back at the house. What about yours?" asked Tim.

"I haven't got one. They cost money." said Nick.

In the moonlight, they could see that the boat was picking up speed.

Nick staggered over to the side of the boat.

"What do we do now?" he asked.

"I don't know," said Tim.

"So all your money can't help us," said Nick.

"It wasn't my money that got us into this mess. It was you and whisky," said Tim.

Nick didn't say a word.

Chapter 5

Tim got to his feet and held onto the side of the boat with one hand. The river was getting wider, and they were about a mile from the sea.

"We could jump in the river and swim for it," said Nick.

Tim shook his head. "The tide's too strong. We'd be swept out to sea.

And I can't swim with one arm,"
he said.

"Well, we have to do something.
We can't just stand here," said Nick.

"Standing here is the best thing we
can do. We're safer on this boat than
swimming in the river. At least people
can see a boat," said Tim.

"But you said this boat wasn't made for
the sea," said Nick.

The way Nick said these words made
Tim look at him. And for the first time that
night, he could see fear in Nick's face.

"What are you looking at?" asked Nick.

"I'm looking at someone who's
frightened," said Tim.

"I'm not frightened," said Nick.

"Yes, you are. So Nick's chicken now,
is he?" said Tim.

Nick was angry but he didn't grab
hold of Tim.

"It's just that I've never been on the sea. What's it like?" he asked.

"You're just about to find out. See those lights over there? That's where it starts," said Tim.

As the boat drifted closer to the sea, it began rocking from side to side. Nick was gripping the side of the boat so hard that his fingers had gone as white as his face. They began shouting at the same time.

"Help, Help!" yelled Tim.

"We need help. Come and get us!" shouted Nick.

"We're drifting out to sea!" shouted Tim.

"Please help us!" yelled Nick.

They yelled and shouted as loudly as they could. But a strong tide was taking the boat quickly away from land. An offshore wind was blowing their voices out to sea. No one shouted back to them.

They drifted further out to sea.

The lights from the houses got smaller and smaller. Nick wiped the sweat from his face. The boat trip had stopped being fun.

"No one can see us and no one can hear us. What are we going to do, Tim?" he asked.

"We're going to hang on for as long as we can," said Tim.

"Hang on to what? If this boat rocks any more we'll be hanging on to the seabed," said Nick.

The houses were now just specks of light. Darkness was all around them. And they didn't know what was out there.

Tim was in pain and beginning to get cold. He made his way into the cabin. Nick followed him in.

"Your dad will come looking when he sees you and the boat are missing, won't he?" asked Nick.

"Yes, but he'll look upriver. I've told you, this boat wasn't made to go out to sea," said Tim.

"But then he'll come down to the sea, won't he?" asked Nick.

"Maybe," said Tim.

"Do you think someone will have seen us drifting out to sea?" asked Nick.

"No. We haven't got lights," said Tim.

"Well, is this boat fitted with a radio so we can speak to someone on land?" asked Nick.

"No," said Tim.

"Have we got rockets or flares?" asked Nick.

"No," said Tim.

"Well, why not?" asked Nick.

"I've told you. This boat is made for the river, not the sea," said Tim.

Nick shouted, "Will you shut up about the river! We're not on the river, we're on the sea and we could die out here!"

Tim shouted back, "And we're on the sea because you got drunk and got into a bad mood. And I've got a broken arm because you got drunk. So don't put the blame on me or this boat."

Tim sat holding his broken arm. Nick stood looking out into the darkness, fear taking over from whisky.

The boat had now drifted three miles along the coast and a mile out to sea. The waves were getting bigger, and the two frightened boys were hanging on as best they could.

"I'm sorry," said Nick.

Tim nodded. Then he said, "Look under your seat. There are two life jackets. They should stop us from drowning if we end up in the sea."

"Oh, great. We won't drown. We'll just die in the freezing cold sea," said Nick.

The boat climbed up to the top of the waves.

Then it dropped down the other side with a thump. It was a bit like being on a ride at a funfair. But they knew they might be paying for this ride with their lives.

The boat pitched and rolled as it struggled to stay upright. It seemed as if each crashing wave was trying to turn the boat over and smash it to bits. Water lashed down onto the deck and came running into the cabin.

Nick picked up anything that wasn't tied down and threw it over the side.

Tim did his best to hang on with one hand. But sometimes he was swung round. Then he cried out in pain as his broken arm hit against the cabin. Nick tried hard to hold on to him.

More water was now getting into the boat.

"Is there a pump to get rid of this water?" shouted Nick.

"Yes, but it works off the engine," said Tim.

"Can't we get rid of it by hand?" asked Nick.

"No way. There's too much coming in. All we can do is hang on and hope someone comes looking for us," said Tim.

"But the sea could be like this for days. I can't hang on for days," said Nick.

"You won't have to. This boat won't last that long," said Tim.

Nick could see that Tim wasn't joking.

"So how long have we got?" he asked.

"I don't know," said Tim.

Nick and Tim hung on as stormy waters pounded their sinking, helpless boat. They looked at the waves crashing into them. They listened to the creaking of wood. Then they took it in turns to be sick!

Chapter 6

Nick saw them first, when the boat was on top of a wave.

"Did you see them?" he shouted.

"See what?" asked Tim.

"Lights. I saw lights out there!" shouted Nick.

The boat climbed up more waves.
But they saw no more lights.

Then, as they got to the top of a very big wave, they both saw them.

"What do you think? Could it be a lifeboat coming to get us?" asked Nick.

Tim said, "I don't know. It might not be a boat at all. The lights could be on land. It's too dark to tell."

"But it could be a boat, couldn't it?" asked Nick.

"If it's a boat, then it's a big one. Small boats wouldn't be out in a sea like this," said Tim.

"But a lifeboat would come out, wouldn't it?" asked Nick.

"Yes, thank goodness. They come out whatever the sea is like," said Tim.

They kept looking for the lights every time they got to the top of a wave. It made them feel that help was close at hand. But it wasn't!

It was Tim who worked it out.

The moon came out and he saw the shape of something he knew.

Nick could tell that Tim had seen something he didn't like.

"What is it, Tim?" he asked.

"It's the one thing we didn't want to see," said Tim.

"What?" asked Nick.

"It's an oil tanker. The biggest thing on the sea. The waves it makes could easily turn us over. They can't see us because we haven't got lights. If it hits us, we're dead," said Tim.

"So what are we going to do?" asked Nick

"We can jump or we can stay. Whichever we do, we'd better start praying," said Tim.

"I'm not jumping into that sea," said Nick.

"That makes two of us," said Tim.

The lights got closer, and the dark shape bigger. It was huge, and it just kept on coming. All they could do was watch, wait and pray. Then the metal hull of the tanker was towering above them, as big as a block of flats.

"We're going to die. We're going to die," said Nick, over and over again.

Tim's mouth was open but he was too frightened to speak.

But just when it seemed they would be crushed under the mighty tanker, the wind turned the small boat and pushed it to one side.

The boat was now pointing towards land. And the waves from the tanker picked it up and rushed it towards the rocky coast. It looked as if it was surfing.

The boat stayed upright for a time. Then it turned on its side and crashed against the rocks.

There was a loud cracking and splintering sound.

Tim fell and cried out in pain. Nick went over to help him as water came rushing into the cabin.

He dragged Tim out and helped him over the side of the boat. They gasped at the coldness of the water.

As each wave came in, it went over their heads. They had to hold their breath until the wave went out again.

"Hang on to the boat. I'll try and get onto the rocks!" shouted Nick.

Tim tried to hang on but his broken arm was being banged against the boat. He had never felt such pain in his life.

"Hold on, hold on!" yelled Nick

Nick made it onto the rocks. Then he jammed his foot into the rocks and held onto the side of the boat. He bent down and grabbed Tim by his lifejacket.

"Come on, Tim. Let go of the boat and grab me with your good hand!" shouted Nick.

Tim gasped for air as another wave hit him.

"Come on, Tim. Let go of the boat. Trust me. I'll pull you up onto the rocks!" shouted Nick.

Tim looked up at Nick. Could he trust him?

"If you stay there you'll drown or get crushed by the boat. Come on!" shouted Nick.

A wave came over the boat and hit Tim. His hand slipped off the boat and Nick pulled as hard as he could.

Tim cried out and the pain made him sick. But Nick didn't stop pulling until they were onto the rocks and well away from the waves.

The sky was clear. The moonlight showed

big waves crashing down onto a boat that was breaking up.

And it showed Nick and Tim flatout on top of the rocks. After a long time Nick got up and looked around.

"You stay here, Tim. I'm going to see what's behind that next lot of rocks," he said.

"You will come back for me, won't you? Don't leave me here," said Tim.

Nick bent down and said, "I got us into this mess. I'll get us out of it. Trust me."

The pain and cold were too much for Tim and he passed out. Nick left him there and went over the rocks and out of sight.

Chapter 7

When Tim came round he couldn't see Nick. Fear gripped him. Just as the fear was turning to panic, Nick came back over the rocks.

"You didn't think I was coming back, did you?" asked Nick. Tim didn't say anything.

"If we can get over these rocks, we can get to a bit of sand under a cliff," said Nick.

"I just want to stay here. My arm hurts like hell every time I move it," said Tim.

"We can't stay here, Tim. It's too cold. We're soaking wet and this wind is making us feel even colder. We could die here. We've got to look for a cave or something," said Nick.

They slowly made their way over the rocks. Nick held onto Tim all the way. At last they stood on the sand and looked around. There was no cave.

"We're going to freeze to death," said Tim. He was cold, wet, tired and in pain.

"No, we're not. If there isn't a cave, we'll make a shelter," said Nick.

"Make a shelter! What with? We've only got sand!" shouted Tim.

"There's always stuff left by high tides. We have to keep the wind off us. It's the wind that's the killer," said Nick.

Tim didn't like that word 'killer'.

He began helping Nick look for things on the sand.

They found logs and smaller bits of wood, two wooden boxes, part of a fishing net, big plastic bags, lots of seaweed, a bucket with no bottom in it, and bits of rope.

Then they dug four big holes in the wet sand. Tim dug one-handed with the help of the broken bucket and Nick helped him with his hands. The digging warmed them up and made them feel better.

They put the longest logs in the holes and packed more sand round them to stop them falling over. They stuck up about three feet off the ground.

Then they put the fishing net over the top and round the sides. Nick used the rope to tie the net to the logs. The smaller bits of wood were stuck upright along the sides of the shelter.

The plastic bags were woven around them to keep the bags upright. Tim helped as well as he could.

"It'll all help to keep out the cold," said Nick.

They put the dry seaweed down and put the wooden boxes on top. Then they crept inside and sat on the boxes.

"I feel a bit better now I'm not so cold. Maybe I can go to sleep," said Tim.

"We're not going to sleep. We have to stay awake all night and not let our body heat drop. If we fall asleep when it's this cold, we may never wake up," said Nick.

"You mean we could die?" asked Tim.

"I mean we could die," said Nick.

"How do you know all this stuff?" asked Tim.

"My dad told me. It was part of his training when he was in the army. They showed him how to live off the land," said Nick.

"What do you mean?" asked Tim.

Nick said, "It means looking after yourself wherever you are. The army trained him to do things like making a shelter and making a fire without matches. He can find fresh water and trap animals. And he knows which plants are safe to eat."

"And did your dad show you how to do all those things?" asked Tim.

"I can do some of them. But I can't make fire without matches," said Nick.

"My dad never seems to have time to show me things. He's always at work making more and more money. I hardly ever see him," said Tim.

Then Tim asked, "So why hasn't your dad got a job, now he's out of the army?"

"Something bad happened to him in the army. Now he can't keep a job for very long," Nick said.

"He keeps getting into bad moods and yelling at people. Then he gets the sack from his job. He hit somebody in his last job. Now he stays in the house most days just looking out of the window. I don't know what's going to happen to him."

"Has he ever told you what happened in the army?" asked Tim.

Nick said, "No, and he hasn't told my mum much about it. He just keeps it all to himself. The army told Mum that he'd been very brave and tried to save his men when they'd been ambushed. Three of his men got killed. The army said there was nothing more my dad could have done. But Dad blames himself for leading his men into the ambush.

"He sometimes shouts out the names of the dead men in his sleep. Then he wakes up and walks around the house for hours.

"It's no good asking him about it.

"He says he'll sort it out by himself. One of his mates comes round every week and they go off drinking. Dad always comes back drunk. Mum and me keep out of his way. Now he's started drinking more and more at home. I think my mum is getting fed up with it."

"How long has your dad been out of the army?" asked Tim.

Nick said, "About a year. He's had five jobs in that time and been sacked from all of them. He says he's not going out looking for more jobs. He keeps on saying he's useless at everything.

"I hate seeing him like this. I want him back like he was. He was a great dad."

Nick was upset. And Tim didn't know what to say. They sat for some time without speaking.

Chapter 8

"So, what about you? What's it like being rich?" asked Nick.

"I don't know," said Tim.

"What do you mean, you don't know? You've got stacks of money," said Nick.

Tim said, "Yes, I know. But it's always been like that for me. I don't think of it as being rich.

"The house we've got is the same size as the houses our friends have got. It's the same with the cars and the boat. We're just the same as our friends. Do you see what I mean?"

"No," said Nick.

"Look. I've always had lots of money. I don't know what it's like not to have money. If I've wanted something I've always been given it."

"Lucky you," said Nick.

Tim went on, "But my dad has never shown me the things yours has. He's never even come fishing with me. I've always wanted him to come but he never has the time. I think that's why he's always giving me things. My mum sometimes tells him that he loves money more than he loves her. Then they have a row. Then they stop speaking to each other. That's when I go off and do things on my own."

Nick began to think that maybe Tim didn't have everything in life after all.

"So what's your school like?" asked Nick.

"It's OK. But it's miles away from home. My dad made me go there. It was the school he went to. I wanted to go to the one down the road. Then I could have had mates close to home," said Tim.

"But you had plenty of mates at your party," said Nick.

"They all go to my school. They came from miles away just for the party," said Tim.

"Why did you ask me to come?" asked Nick.

"I saw you bringing our newspaper every day. You seemed OK," said Tim.

Nick could see that Tim was shivering, so he took off his jacket and put it round him.

"No, take it back. You've got to keep warm as well," said Tim.

"I can run around to keep warm. You can't with your broken arm," said Nick.

Tim kept the jacket on. Nick ran around outside.

When he came back into the shelter, the two of them started talking again. They kept on talking until night turned into day. By that time they knew a lot about each other. They also knew that if they got out of this alive, they would be mates forever.

Chapter 9

As soon as it was light Nick went out to have a look around. Then he came back in to see how Tim was getting on.

Tim was in great pain from his broken arm. His face was white and he looked very tired.

Nick sat down and said, "It's not looking good. There's nothing left of the boat.

"It must have broken up. The bits have sunk or drifted out to sea. No one is going to know where to look for us. It could be days before they find us. We haven't got days. We've no fresh water or food. And we've got to get you to a hospital as fast as we can. We could stay here and hope. But we'd just get weaker, day by day."

"So what do we do?" asked Tim.

"I've got to try and get up that cliff and get to a house. Then we can get some help," said Nick

Tim stepped out of the shelter and looked up at a cliff that seemed to go on forever. It was very steep and very rocky.

"Up there!" said Tim. "Do you think you can make it, Nick?"

"I don't know. I've been rock climbing with my dad. I'm not bad at it," said Nick. Tim didn't know what to say. The climb looked much too hard.

But it was the only way out. No one could swim in that stormy sea.

"Your dad would be proud of you, right now," said Tim.

"He wouldn't be proud of me getting us into this mess," said Nick.

They both walked over to the cliff and stood looking up at it.

Nick said, "Keep yourself warm and don't give up hope. And don't drink the seawater, however thirsty you get."

"OK," said Tim.

"Well, here I go," said Nick.

"Good luck," said Tim.

Nick took his time looking for a good handhold on the rock. Then he pulled himself up the first bit of cliff. His long climb had begun.

The first part was easy. There were lots of cracks in the rock for him to get hold of. He was soon part way up the cliff.

He felt strong and he was pleased at the way he was climbing.

Tim was also pleased as he stood looking up.

"Maybe he'll make it, after all," he said to himself.

But then the climb got harder as Nick started up a big slab of rock. There were less and less handholds and he soon had to stop climbing.

He was now hanging onto the rock trying to work out what to do. There had to be a hold somewhere, but where? He looked and looked, but he couldn't see one. He was stuck.

Nick looked down. But he knew there was no going back. It was harder going down than it was going up. He had to go on. But how?

His arms and legs were killing him from having to hang on for so long.

His hands were wet with sweat.

Fear crept into his mind. How long could he hang on like this? How long before he slipped off the rock and fell to his death?

Nick shook his head. What would his dad tell him to do? He'd say, "Keep looking for that handhold. And if you can't see one, feel for one with your hand."

Nick slid his hand over the rock.

"I can't find one, Dad. I can't find one!" he cried out.

Then the tips of his fingers felt a small gap in the rock. He would have to reach up to get a good grip. But it gave him hope.

But as he reached up, his left foot slipped off the rock. Bits of rock fell all the way down the cliff and landed at Tim's feet. Tim put his hand over his mouth to stop himself from crying out.

Nick was now hanging on by his right hand and right foot.

His left hand was on the rock feeling for the hold again. He was scraping his left foot against the rock trying to find some grip.

He couldn't stay like this for much longer. His hand and arm were hurting like hell. But then he found the fingertip hold. And he clung on until he got his left foot back onto the rock as well.

Now he could see more handholds and he pulled himself up bit by bit.

He stopped and rested on the top of the slab of rock. He was soaked with sweat and his lungs were on fire. His legs were shaking and he'd got cramp in his hands and arms.

That short climb had been the biggest test of his life. He had never been so frightened.

"Thanks, Dad," he said out loud.

When he felt stronger, he set off again.

The next bit was more like scrambling than rock climbing. He dug his fingers and feet into the short grass and loose soil, and pulled himself up. Then came another rocky bit, but it was easy.

"I'm going to do it. I got us into this mess but I'm going to get us out again," he said aloud. But as he climbed up to the next ridge, a wall of rock faced him.

"Don't panic. Just think what Dad would do," he said to himself. He stood planning and plotting his way up the granite rock.

"Here we go, again," he said, as he set off.

It tested his skills to the limit. But he made it. He smiled. Ahead of him was a grassy slope and it looked easy to climb.

"When I get up that, I should be looking at the top of the cliff," he said, to himself. He was. But what he saw took the smile off his face.

The climb to the cliff top wasn't far. But he might as well have been climbing to the moon. It was impossible!

The climb wasn't made of rock. It was clay and sand, with small stones sticking out of it.

It would just fall apart if he tried to climb it. The cliff top was a big overhang. Nobody could get up and over that without being helped by rope.

It took a second for the shock to hit him. He had nowhere to go. He was stuck. It was too hard to go back and impossible to go on. His rescue act was at an end. He was now as helpless as Tim.

He sat down. There was no hope. He sat very still, trying not to panic.

"What the hell am I going to do?" he asked himself.

As he sat, he looked up at the last bit of cliff.

Birds had pecked holes in the clay and were using them for nesting. Some of the birds took off and flew around the cliff tops.

"If only I could do that," Nick said to himself.

Then some of the birds flew closer to him. It was nesting time and they didn't want him near their eggs.

The birds swooped down and screeched at him.

"I'm not after your eggs, you stupid birds. Leave me alone!" he shouted.

But more and more birds joined in. Long, sharp beaks flashed past him, getting ever closer to his head.

It seemed as if the whole cliff was alive with them.

Nick put his hands over his head. It wasn't fair. Everything seemed to be against him.

He flattened himself on the ground, and yelled at them again.

But the more he yelled, the more the birds dived and screamed at him.

And that's what saved him.

Chapter 10

Jane Fisher kept her eye to the telescope as she looked for boats out at sea. She had been scanning the waves for three hours. But all she had seen was a stormy sea and dark clouds.

Her shift in the Coast Watch Station was coming to an end. She could hear Tom Wilson climbing up the steps to take over.

She and Tom kept the lookout station open. They didn't get paid for their work but they helped save lives every year. Just like the many other lookout stations around the coast of Britain.

"Seen anything this morning?" asked Tom, as he stepped inside the room.

"Waves, water and weather. I'm off home for lunch," said Jane. She put on her coat and looked across at her dog.

"Come on, you. Time for a walk," she said. The boxer sprang to its feet at the word 'walk'.

"I'll go the long way home and give this lazy lump a bit of a run. See you, Tom," said Jane.

Jane let her dog off the lead as she walked along the coast path. He ran ahead sniffing and peeing. The sky was now very dark and rain began to fall. Then it came down by the bucketful.

After about a mile she took the path going inland. She looked back to see where her dog had got to. He was close to the edge of the cliff.

"Come on, you daft dog. I'm getting soaked!" shouted Jane. The dog was now looking over the cliff and barking like mad. Birds were diving down making a lot of noise.

"Come here and stop upsetting the birds!" she shouted. The dog kept on barking.

"If I have to come over and get you, you're not having any dinner," she shouted at him.

Jane had to go over and get him. As she grabbed hold of him she said, "I told you to . . ." That's when she saw Nick.

"Good God! You frightened the life out of me. What are you doing down there? Did you fall over the edge?" she asked.

"I've climbed up from the beach,"
said Nick.

"You can't have. It's too hard," Jane said.
Then she took a good look at him. He was
soaking wet and shivering with cold.
He looked shattered.

"Please help me. I can't get up this last
bit. And my friend's down on the beach
with a broken arm," said Nick.

"Hang on. My mobile doesn't work out
here. I've got to get back to the lookout
station to get help. It's a mile away.
I'll be back as quickly as I can," said Jane.
She started to run back to the station.

Nick sat looking up at an empty sky.
Had he been dreaming? Was he really
going to be saved by a dog chasing birds?

Forty minutes later, he was being roped
up the last bit of cliff. Blankets were put
round him and he was helped into the
back of a Land Rover.

Jane and her dog got in as well.

"We've contacted the lifeboat station and an inshore craft will pick up your friend. He'll be taken to hospital. We're going there now so you can have a checkup," said Jane.

Nick was still shivering, but he smiled at her and patted the dog.

"I'm glad he chases birds. What's his name?" asked Nick.

"Whisky," said Jane. Nick's smile turned into a laugh.

"What's so funny?" asked Jane.

"It was whisky that got me into this mess. And it's Whisky that's saved me," he said.

Look out for other exciting stories in the
Survival series:

Runaway

Is Joe's dad still alive?

After no word from his dad for two years, Joe decides to go to the last place his dad was seen: Hong Kong.

Joe's story continues in 'The Boss'.

The Boss

Alone and afraid in Liverpool, Joe gets involved with a gang of drug pushers.

With no money, food or shelter Joe is an easy target for The Boss.

Joe's story begins in 'Runaway'.

Why Me?

'The gang saw him run, and gave a cheer. Showing fear was just what they wanted to see. It fed their hunger for power.'

When Wayne starts a new school his life is made hell by a group of bullies.

Will they beat him down, or can he fight back?

Fireproof

"I'll burn this school down one day. You see if I don't."

When Jack's school burns down that night the police come looking for him.

But did he do it?

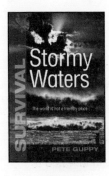

Stormy Waters

"I'm glad I don't fit in here. I hate rich people like you," yelled Nick.

Nick wants revenge. He takes Tim's boat but the prank soon turns into a nightmare.

How will the nightmare end?

The Gambling Habit

Gambling is the best feeling in the world for Steve. He's lying, stealing and shoplifting from one bet to the next.

What will it take to show him that there is more to life than gambling?

Jet Scream

Day 1 . . .
The 52 people sitting on the plane
knew they were going to die.

Ben and Jane are the only survivors of
the plane crash. Will they be able to
stay alive?

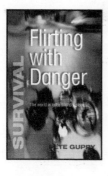

Flirting with Danger

Amrit and Jenny get their first taste of
freedom as they head off on a
backpacking trip away from their
families.

But the fun soon turns to fear . . .

About the author

Have you ever been hunted by the police, chased by a gang, or tried to stay alive after a plane crash?

If you have, then you know the name of the game is survival. If you haven't, why not read about the teenagers in my stories. They find getting into trouble is easy. It's the getting out of trouble that's the hard bit.

I spent three years training to be a teacher and 33 years being one. I always wanted to know how hard it would be to write books for teenagers. Now I know!

Pete Guppy

SURVIVAL

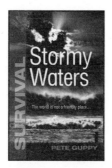